Why is Grandma a STRANGER to Me?

Andrea River

Paperback: 978-1-80227-066-2
eBook: 978-1-80227-067-9

For my children

and dedicated to the memory

of their grandmother,

forever in my heart.

"Who is that lady in the photo?" asked Sophie one day.

"That's your dear grandma," Sophie's mum did say.

"But why is Grandma a stranger to me?

Can she come over later, to play
and have tea?"

"No darling, she lives in another place.

She left here when it was time, to rest and have space."

"But where, Mummy? Can we visit her? Visit her soon?"

"No dear, she's in a place, further away than the moon."

"I never met Grandma, did I? But I miss her so.
I miss the lady, who I never got to know.
We could have painted a brightly coloured rainbow,
Or watched my sunflowers and strawberry plants grow.

"I feel angry, Mummy, and so very teary.

You must feel sad and perhaps a little weary?"

"You are right, Sophie, some days can still be tough.

But I have you now, which is more than enough.

"Grandma left this world before you were born.

Mummy was so sad. Her tears made a rainstorm.

But Sophie, you're wrong about one thing, I'm sure.

You do know your grandma. I'll show you…. let's explore.

"Here is our kitchen, where we often bake

Banana bread, lemon and chocolate cake.

We stir the ingredients in her old mixing bowl.

In every treat we make, shines a little of her soul.

"Do you remember what I make, when you are ill?

To fight off the winter bugs and colds or a chill?

Your favourite, chicken soup, from your grandma's own recipe.

Exactly how she made it, all those years ago for me.

"It is a recipe made with so much love.

She is comforting and nourishing you from above.

Next time you have some, remember to savour

Its extra special smell, taste and flavour.

"I have passed on to you this magic remedy.

Next, let's think about Grandma's favourite melody.

She liked a cheerful song, with a happy tune.

Perhaps you could play the piano, this afternoon?

"She would tell you how important music is to play.

It can brighten up the dullest or saddest day.

Every time you play a note on the keys,

She would be so proud and pleased.

"Now, let's take a walk, in the garden outside.

Here is the rose bush I planted, when she died.

Every time it begins to flower and bloom,

Its glorious scent smells just like her perfume.

"Her garden was her place, of calm and peace.

Surrounded by nature, the birds and the bees.

Sophie, when you grow vegetables on your patch,

The joy that it gives you, is hard to match.

"Shall we take a few steps further, to our summer house?

It's so quiet in there, you could hear the squeak of a mouse.

On a bench like this, she would tell me her childhood tales:

Pirate games, treehouses and the search for secret trails.

"Once, in the forest, she met a real bear.

She screamed and ran home, from the terrible scare.

In winter, on a frozen lake, she learned how to skate.

In spring, real eggs for Easter, she would paint and decorate.

"In summer and autumn, she picked berries and sloes

And turned them into jam, or a drink to warm her toes.

At Christmas, she would light real candles on the tree.

One year, the tree caught light and we all had to flee.

"It's these stories and traditions, that we must never forget.

They connect us together like a woven net.

You see Sophie, you do know your grandma, it's true.

There's so much of HER that lives on in YOU."

THE END

Ingram Content Group UK Ltd.
Milton Keynes UK
UKHW052013140423
420213UK00002B/31

9 781802 270662